MY PERSONAL PLANNER

—TRIBUTES—

"*My Personal Planner* is a great way to put end-of-life affairs in order so your family will know your wishes. You create a thoughtful gift for yourself now and help reduce emotional stress and suffering for survivors at the time of your death."

——**Liz Bennett**, free lance writer
Former Book Editor, *The Houston Post*

"It takes a lot of foresight and gumption to make this neglected subject so easy to navigate, but you did it in an upbeat way. It's great."

——**Scotty MacLeod**, retired executive, Billings, Montana

"You help us remember that our movement out of this world is full of important opportunities. Thanks for writing a book to help us live and die in the most noble and purposeful ways."

——**Rev. Dr. David Peterson**, Senior Pastor
Memorial Drive Presbyterian Church, Houston, Texas

"Margie Jenkins' book is a wonderfully insightful, easy-to-read journey through the things that we all treasure about life, especially at the end of life. She interweaves her personal experiences…to illustrate that death is not something to shut away in a closet, treated as 'life's most overlooked milestone'."

——**Nancy Borst**, writer, Kansas City, Kansas

"I can't tell you how important your book is to me. Losing my parents over the last few years made me realize that death is just another part of life, but we need to plan for it…."

——**Kimberly Wallace**, seminar attendee, Houston, Texas

MY PERSONAL PLANNER

EXPANDED EDITION

FOR USE WITH THE BOOK

PREPARING FOR THE END OF LIFE
WITH GRACE AND GUSTO

MARGIE JENKINS

BALCONY PUBLISHING
Georgetown, TX 78627

MY PERSONAL PLANNER
EXPANDED EDITION

Copyright © 2009 Margie Little Jenkins

Published by: Balcony Publishing, Inc.
P.O. Box 2175, Georgetown, TX 78627

Library of Congress
Catalog Card Number (Applied For)
ISBN 978-0-929488-78-3

Acknowledgement: The author and publisher greatfully acknowledge permission from Bob Bolton to use his photograph of Margie and Bob Jenkins on the back cover of this book.

Printed in the United States of America
2nd printing: October 2010
10 9 8 7 6 5 4 3 2

LOVINGLY DEDICATED

To each of you who honors
your loved ones by preparing
for the end of your life with
Grace and **Gusto**

CONTENTS ONE

CONTENTS TWO

INTRODUCTION

Why End-of-Life Planning is Important

Dying is an equal opportunity event. Everyone gets to do it. There is no way out. Those who think dying is solely for the elderly need only look at obituary pages in newspapers. There, people of all ages are listed—from infants to those over 100. Since dying is inevitable, *making end-of-life decisions before it's too late is a wonderful gift* **to those you love**, *and* **to yourself**.

More than 100 decisions must be made within a very short time of a person's death. That's why *gathering essential information* **now** *will reduce trauma, confusion, and suffering for your survivors when your departure time arrives.* Many people think a will is the only thing needed at death. Although a will is very important, there is so much more. What kind of funeral would you prefer, and where do you want to be buried? How do you want to be remembered? Who should be notified when you die? How should your cherished possessions be distributed? No one will know this information unless decisions and preferences are made by you, written down, and kept in a location known to your loved ones.

The Book, *You Only Die Once*

You Only Die Once is a sensitive, candid, and uplifting experience. It uses heart-warming stories, amusing anecdotes, and comfortable suggestions to inspire you to complete your own personal end-of-life plan—a plan that avoids pitfalls that await your family if you do not adequately prepare for this inescapable event. *You Only Die Once* is also a comprehensive and easily accessible resource to help you work your way through this planner.

My Personal Planner

My Personal Planner is a hands-on road map that presents an exciting opportunity to create your own master end-of-life plan. It provides checklists, surveys, forms to fill out, questions to answer, and guidelines to assist you in personalizing your plan. This experience leads you step by step through the decision-making process. It also gives you powerful input regarding how you want to be treated at the end. You become a responsible participant in preparing for life's ending as a culmination of living well, instead of viewing death as an unplanned event.

Using *My Personal Planner*

As you go through *My Personal Planner,* while referring to related chapters in *You Only Die Once,* your written personal choices will be a valuable record for your family. Do it step by step, and don't rush yourself. Setting time goals will be helpful. Completing the planner is an ongoing process. Talking with your family about what you are doing—and where you keep this important information— provides meaningful conversation. It also makes it much more likely that your plans will be followed after you are gone.

You can make your end-of-life plan without using every page in this planner. For instance, you may not choose to have a burial service. Or, there may be a financial form that does not fit your circumstances. Select items in *My Personal Planner* that are most suitable to you, and use them. In some cases, you may want to create your own forms.

Keep in mind that when spouses are working together on their plan, each of them often will need to make separate forms. For example, this will be true when filling out their medical crisis forms or writing their own obituaries.

Recording your specific choices in *My Personal Planner* enables you to write a comprehensive end-of-life plan. It provides a thoughtful gift to your survivors, and affords you a satisfying and interesting journey through the planning process.

Both life and death are miracles to examine, mysteries to explore, and bodacious adventures to dare.

AVOID THE SCAVENGER HUNT

Have you ever been on a "scavenger hunt", where you are given a list of items to find? It can be a fun game—but not when you are searching for important documents at the time of a crisis. Complete the "Location-Location-Location" form on page 11, and your loved ones will avoid a scavenger hunt for some of the most important items they will need at the time of your medical crisis or death.

You may not have some of the requested items yet. If so, record as much of this information as you *do* have. Then give copies of the "Location-Location Location" form to trusted persons of your choosing. Having done this, you may take all the time necessary to put together your end-of-life plan, aware that if you should become incapacitated during that process, your loved ones will know exactly where to find these critical documents. This will be all-important if you unexpectedly experience a life threatening accident or disease... or death. So don't hold back this information during the weeks or months it may take you to work on your entire end-of-life plan.

To some people, things like wills and advance directives are very private. While making this information accessible for dire emergencies, you may want to keep it secure until such incidents occur or until other times of your choosing. To ease your concerns about privacy, read #5 on page 11 before you start to work on the other items.

If the only thing you do with *My Personal Planner* is fill out page 11 and give it to your closest relative and your executor, your loved ones will be much better prepared for your end-of-life events than the great majority of families. Give them this thoughtful and loving present...and avoid the scavenger hunt!

LOCATION-LOCATION-LOCATION

NAME:_____

1. THE LOCATION(S) OF **MY INSURANCE POLICIES:**

_____

_____

2. THE LOCATION(S) OF **MY WILL:**

_____

_____

3. THE LOCATION(S) OF **MY ADVANCE DIRECTIVES:**

_____

_____

4. THE NAME, ADDRESS, E-MAIL ADDRESS, AND PHONE NUMBER(S) OF **MY EXECUTOR:**

_____

_____

5. PERMISSION TO ACCESS **MY PRIVATE DOCUMENTS:**

I have provided the above information so that, in case of my incapacitation or death, my loved ones will be able to locate and examine my private end-of-life documents. However, prior to either of these events, no one is permitted to access this information without my express permission.

Note: If there is anything on this page you cannot answer, complete as much information as you can. Then distribute copies to close family members and your executor. As you work on your end-of-life plan, you will discover answers you don't know right now. When this occurs, be sure to update this form and advise the very important people in your life.

CREATING A MASTER END-OF-LIFE PLAN

How can you "straighten up and die right"? There are many issues to consider, like: What are some things you want to do before you die? Who should receive your treasured possessions? Are your vital papers up-to-date? What kind of funeral best reflects your wishes? Chapter 2 of *You Only Die Once* deals with end-of-life planning. I suggest you read through this chapter before you begin creating your own plan.

Preparing for your end-of-life adventure does not have to be an intimidating task. Try something as easy as this: Get a bunch of file folders and keep them handy as you read through *My Personal Planner,* selecting the planning forms that work for you. (I like color, so my files are rainbow-like.) Simply write a subject name on a folder tab each time you decide to gather information on an end-of-life topic. The list on page 13 will get you started. Keep your folders in alphabetical order and you are on your way. As you work on your plan—or just go about daily business—collect any information you come across that seems pertinent to a particular subject. Put the information in your related subject folder, and it will be there when you begin work in that specific area. Over time, these file folders will become your master end-of-life plan—greatly reducing the suffering and panic that death causes. Name your plan to make it more personal. Names I have heard are: Final Chorus, Last Expedition, and 19th Hole.

You may keep your documents in a box, a drawer, a closet, or at the office. Tell your family that you are creating a file of end-of-life decisions, and let them know where it is located. Then have family discussions about this inevitable event. Your master file system may also be kept on your computer, but be sure someone knows how to access the file. Otherwise, it might be useless.

As you create your master end-of-life plan, you will discover a great sense of satisfaction and accomplishment—and the healing power of knowing you are preparing a wonderful gift for your survivors before you say good-bye.

END-OF-LIFE PLANNING FILE

Reviewing the list below will help you select the subjects for folders to go into your end-of-life file. Use only the ones that fit your plan. Add subjects you need that I have not included. Organize your folders (perhaps alphabetically) into a readily available master file system. Make sure your collection of folders includes one for each of the forms from *My Personal Planner* that you choose to complete.

Advance Directives

Attorney

Bank Accounts

Benefits

Birth Certificate

Bodacious Living Ideas

Bonds/Securities

Brokerage Accounts

Burial Information

Car/Vehicle Titles

Cherished Possessions

Contracts

CPA

Divorce Papers

Financial Statements

Funeral/Cemetery Information

Going-Away-Party Reception

Hospice

Instant Action Folder

Insurance Policies

Inventory of Belongings

Loans

Long Term Care

Marriage License

Medical Crisis Information

Memorial/Funeral Service

Military Papers

Mortgages

My Support Circle

Obituary

Passwords (computers, etc.)

Pensions

People to Notify

Real Estate Titles and Deeds

Safe Deposit Box(s)

Social Security/Medicare Information

Stages of Grief

Tax Returns (past 4 years)

"Ten-Best-Things" List

Things I Want To Do Before I Die

When Death Occurs, What to Do

Will and Executor

IMPORTANT! Include name, address, phone number, FAX number, and e-mail address for individuals and businesses where contact information is needed.

INSTANT ACTION FOLDER

Emergency Information

Congratulations! You are now putting together your overall end-of-life plan. The approach to this plan suggested in *You Only Die Once* (see Chapter 2) likely will involve dozens of folders on particular topics. When arranged all together in alphabetical order, they become your personal end-of-life plan.

But, before you accumulate everything essential to your overall plan, it is vitally important to gather the information for the very first folder—the "Instant Action Folder". This will contain the information your loved ones will need to start using immediately at the time of your medical crisis or death. It is data that family members should have "right now"— but usually are searching for, here and there, and don't find until long after it could have helped them most. These are what I call your *vital papers*.

You may decide to place these vital papers in a single file folder. Or, it may be better to make it your "Instant Action Section", with several folders, each containing different vital papers—all located at the front of your end-of-life file.

Being informed is crucial, especially when it's about things that matter most. Many married couples keep secrets from one another. Sometimes, it is only when a crisis strikes that a spouse realizes he/she does not have essential basic knowledge such as: medical crisis information; what to do first when death occurs; the location of advanced directives; and your executor's name and phone number. These important items make up your top priority "Instant Action Folder" (or file section)—information needed immediately at the time of crisis or death.

I encourage you to make the "Instant Action Folder" your first step in developing your overall end-of-life plan. As you work on this activity, read through Chapter 4* of *You Only Die Once,* where these vital papers are discussed in detail. Completing the next few pages will provide essential information for the most important areas in your end-of-life plan.

My Personal Planner was written after the book, *You Onle Die Once*. The treatment of the "Instant Action Folder" in the planner is more complete than in the book. —Margie Jenkins—

INSTANT ACTION FOLDER

Contents

No matter how well prepared you are for the medical crisis or death of a loved one, it is always an incredibly profound and mystical experience. When it happens, those who are in charge have to start doing things. But what? What should be done first?

This is when your "Instant Action Folder" becomes extremely important. Your objective in preparing it is to give your family/friends an instant plan so they can calm themselves, get help promptly, and take the steps you prefer in your time of crisis or death.

The next few pages give you forms to fill out that can place all this information in the hands of your loved ones only minutes after the onset of such events. Yes, preparing this information may be difficult, even painful; but it will be far less painful for you to do it *now* than for your loved ones to be without it in the midst of their grief. Following is a list of forms and documents you will prepare for your "Instant Action Folder":

1. MEDICAL CRISIS FORM

2. WALLET CARD

3. WHEN DEATH OCCURS, WHAT TO DO

4. ADVANCE DIRECTIVES

You give a real blessing to your loved ones when you have these forms and documents completed and readily available. And when you have told them where this information is located. My husband and I keep our instant action data in a red file folder—in front of our master end-of-life plan in a kitchen drawer. Our kids know where it is.

Where would be the best place for you to keep **your** vital information?

MEDICAL CRISIS FORM

This project deserves your attention now!

I hope you don't have to face a serious medical crisis. You have enough going on in your life without a major disruption caused by a health problem or accident. But they happen—and at the least convenient times. Ha! As if any crisis is ever welcome or timely. I don't even like the word *crisis*.

The worst part is you don't have a clue about when, where, or how it will happen. Or what it will feel like. A medical crisis is upsetting to everyone involved, and normally it is costly in terms of repair time and dollars. Then there is the possibility of long term or total disability.

In light of all this, I'm convinced it will be worth your while to give this topic considerable thought—and some serious planning. I've composed the form on pages 17-19 to help ease you through this process. Since we can't outlaw medical emergencies, I strongly suggest you do your loved ones and yourself a favor and fill out the "Medical Crisis Form" as soon as possible. You will be much better prepared for the days ahead.

In addition to completing this form, there are other things to consider: insurance, staying in reasonably good physical condition, having periodical medical check-ups, and practicing mindfulness. Since most accidents occur at home, it is important to follow safety measures in your house and yard to a practical extent. Little things, like good lighting and grab bars in bathrooms and at steps, can make a big difference.

Whenever immediate hospital or physician attention is required, the first thing they do is ask you to fill out a form for information about your medical history, medications you take, signed advance directives, other doctor's names, and whom to notify in case of emergency. If you have this medical information already available, it can save you time and trauma—and even prevent death. It will reduce stress and anxiety and help you receive faster medical service.

Location is important. You should keep copies of this completed form in your "Instant Action Folder", at some spot known to everyone in your home, and in your car. Give copies to other appropriate people. Be sure to update your "Medical Crisis Form" whenever important medical changes occur.

MEDICAL CRISIS FORM

Reminder: Each spouse should fill out a separate copy of this form.

PURPOSE: This form will help you collect information to have readily available in case of a medical crisis. Keep a copy in your home where you and your significant others know the location. And in your car, in the glove compartment with your automobile insurance ID card—even in your purse or briefcase. In an emergency room situation, this important information could help doctors act more quickly and efficiently, and perhaps *even save your life*.

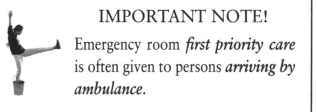

IMPORTANT NOTE!
Emergency room *first priority care* is often given to persons *arriving by ambulance*.

1. PERSONAL INFORMATION:

   YOUR NAME_____DATE OF BIRTH_____

   ADDRESS_____

   HOME PHONE_____WORK PHONE_____

   CELL PHONE_____E-MAIL_____

   SOCIAL SECURITY NUMBER_____BLOOD TYPE_____

2. PRIMARY MEDICAL INSURANCE COMPANY:

   COMPANY NAME_____POLICY NUMBER_____

   ADDRESS_____PHONE NUMBER_____

3. SECONDARY MEDICAL INSURANCE COMPANY:

   COMPANY NAME_____POLICY NUMBER_____

   ADDRESS_____PHONE NUMBER_____

4. PERSON TO NOTIFY IN CASE OF EMERGENCY (and alternate person):

   NAME_____RELATIONSHIP_____PHONE_____

   CELL_____WORK PHONE_____E-MAIL_____

   ALTERNATE NAME _____RELATIONSHIP_____PHONE_____

   CELL_____WORK PHONE_____E-MAIL_____

MEDICAL CRISIS FORM

5. CLOSEST HOSPITAL:

HOSPITAL NAME_____PHONE NUMBER_____

ADDRESS_____E. R. LOCATION_____

6. SPECIALITY HOSPITAL(S) (relating to specific needs and preferences):

HOSPITAL NAME_____PHONE NUMBER_____

ADDRESS_____E. R. LOCATION_____

SPECIFIC NEEDS_____

_____

7. NAME/PHONE NO. OF PHYSICIANS AND WHAT MEDICAL TREATMENT THEY PROVIDE:

_____

_____

_____

8. MEDICATIONS:

MEDICINE NAME	PURPOSE	DOSAGE	FREQUENCY	HOW LONG USED

MEDICAL CRISIS FORM

9. SURGERIES (type, purpose, physicians, and date):

_____

_____

_____

10. MEDICAL PROBLEMS/ALLERGIES:

_____

_____

11. ADVANCE DIRECTIVES AND LOCATIONS (Check {√} the advance directives you have {see pages 26-30} and note where each is located):

A. **STATUTORY DURABLE POWER OF ATTORNEY** Yes___No___ Location_____
        (√)   (√)

B. **MEDICAL POWER OF ATTY. FOR HEALTH CARE** Yes___No___ Location_____
        (√)   (√)

C. **DIRECTIVE TO PHYSICIANS AND FAMILY OR SURROGATES (LIVING WILL)** Yes___No___ Location_____
        (√)   (√)

D. **APPOINTMENT OF AGENT TO CONTROL DISPOSITION OF REMAINS** Yes___No___ Location_____
        (√)   (√)

E. **APPOINTMENT OF GUARDIAN FOR MINORS, AND/OR DISABLED ADULTS** Yes___No___ Location_____
        (√)   (√)

F. **OUT-OF-HOSPITAL (OOH) DO NOT RESUSCITATE (DNR) ORDER** Yes___No___ Location_____
        (√)   (√)

G. **OTHER ADVANCE DIRECTIVES**

_____ Yes___No___ Location_____
        (√)   (√)

_____ Yes___No___ Location_____
        (√)   (√)

12. ANY OTHER PERTINENT MEDICAL INFORMATION:

_____

_____

WALLET CARD

Don't leave home without it!

The wallet card is a simplified version of your "Medical Crisis Form" from the previous pages. It can be carried in your wallet/purse at all times. To protect it, you may also have it laminated.

Some people have modified and enlarged them to fit their needs. Be sure to tell your family and friends about your wallet card and where you keep it. Then, in case of emergencies, they will know where to look for it.

Many times, when a crisis occurs, the person is confused, unable to speak, or give vital information. In such situations, the wallet card provides essential data for medical professionals.

Make a copy of the wallet card on the next page, fill it out, and carry it at all times. You might even carry one copy on your person and keep another in the glove compartment of your car. This safety measure should get you faster medical attention and might even save your life. Be sure to update it when the information changes.

For more information about the importance of the wallet card, read Chapter 4 of *You Only Die Once*.

WALLET CARD

PURPOSE: In case of emergencies, it is advisable to carry an ID card with essential medical information in your wallet, purse, or on your person so assistance can be called and help rendered.

INSTRUCTIONS:
- Make a copy of this page.
- Using the information on your "Medical Crisis Form", fill out the cards.
- Cut them out along the solid black lines; then fold them in the middle.
- If you wish to laminate your cards, trim the laminate material flush with the shaded area. Then it will be the same size as your driver's license and credit cards.
- Carry it in your wallet or purse and, perhaps, keep a copy in your glove compartment.

GRAY AREA INDICATES 1/8 INCH LAMINATED EDGE AFTER TRIMMING.

In Case of Emergency	
Name:_____	Med. Insurance: _____
Address:_____	Doctor:_____
Home Phone:_____	Allergies:_____
Spouse/Other Name:_____	Health Problems:_____
Spouse/Other Phone:_____	Medications:_____
Blood Type:_____	Advance Directives Location:_____

FRONT   BACK

(Extra Copy)

GRAY AREA INDICATES 1/8 INCH LAMINATED EDGE AFTER TRIMMING.

In Case of Emergency	
Name:_____	Med. Insurance: _____
Address:_____	Doctor:_____
Home Phone:_____	Allergies:_____
Spouse/Other Name:_____	Health Problems:_____
Spouse/Other Phone:_____	Medications:_____
Blood Type:_____	Advance Directives Location:_____

FRONT   BACK

WHEN DEATH OCCURS, WHAT TO DO

Why This is Important

The death of a loved one causes the most difficult moments in a person's life.

Nothing ever adequately prepares us for the initial shock. Feelings of panic and help-lessness can be overwhelming. The emotional impact and numbness often make it difficult to concentrate on the onerous details associated with what needs to be done at the time of a death.

Immediate Action is Necessary

Complete the "When Death Occurs, What to Do" form *before* there is a need. Then, when death *does* occur, your loved ones, who normally might be stunned and direc-tionless, will be able to act quickly and decisively. It will be a wonderful guide, helping them to know what to do at this traumatic time.

Fill in as much of the information as you can. After you are finished, make two copies. Place one in your "When Death Occurs, What To Do" folder—and be *sure* to place the other copy in your "Instant Action" folder. Tell your significant others where you keep this document.

Good Results Will Follow

Your death will be less confusing and painful for your survivors if you complete this form now. You will leave them a loving blessing.

WHEN DEATH OCCURS, WHAT TO DO

Important Information for Survivors*

1. CALL 911—IF DEATH IS APPARENT OR UNCERTAIN:

   A. THE 911 DISPATCHER WILL SEND EMERGENCY SERVICE TO THE SCENE.

   B. IF DEATH HAS OCCURED, AN EMERGENCY SERVICE ATTENDANT WILL CERTIFY DEATH.

   C. IF THE PATIENT IS ALIVE, AN EMERGENCY SERVICE ATTENDANT WILL RENDER APPROPRIATE CARE.

2. IN THE EVENT OF UNUSUAL CIRCUMSTANCES (accident, crime, suicide):

   A. THE 911 DISPATCHER WILL SEND AN OFFICER OF THE LAW TO THE SCENE.

   B. DO NOT DISTURB OR MOVE THE BODY UNTIL AN OFFICER OF THE LAW PERMITS.

3. TWO PEOPLE TO CALL FOR IMMEDIATE SUPPORT:

   NAME_____ PHONE_____

   NAME_____ PHONE_____

4. CALL HOSPICE (if involved):

   NAME_____ PHONE_____

5. IMMEDIATE FAMILY MEMBERS TO NOTIFY:

   NAME_____ PHONE_____

   NAME_____ PHONE_____

   NAME_____ PHONE_____

   NAME_____ PHONE_____

   NAME_____ PHONE_____

   NAME_____ PHONE_____

6. CALL PASTOR/PLACE OF WORSHIP:

   NAME_____ PHONE_____

7. CALL THE PERSON WHO HAS AUTHORITY TO HAVE THE BODY REMOVED:

   NAME_____ PHONE_____

8. CALL MORTUARY TO PICK UP BODY:

   MORTUARY NAME_____ PHONE_____

*Name alternates when appropriate. Attach extra pages where needed.

WHEN DEATH OCCURS, WHAT TO DO

9. CONTACT MORTUARY ABOUT FUNERAL/MEMORIAL SERVICE AND BURIAL/CREMATION:

NAME OF MORTUARY_____PHONE_____

ADDRESS_____

10. CONTACT CEMETERY:

NAME OF CEMETERY_____

ADDRESS_____ PHONE_____

11. WILL LOCATION(S):_____

12. ADVANCE DIRECTIVES LOCATION(S):

_____

13. NOTIFY EXECUTOR THAT DEATH HAS OCCURRED:

NAME OF EXECUTOR_____

PHONE_____CELL PHONE_____

ALTERNATE EXECUTOR_____

PHONE_____CELL PHONE_____

14. NOTIFY FAMILY ATTORNEY:

NAME OF ATTORNEY_____

PHONE_____CELL PHONE_____

15. INSURANCE INFORMATION:

A. NOTIFY LIFE INSURANCE AGENT

Company Name_____

Agent's Name_____Phone_____

Policy Number_____Amount Payable at Death_____

Location of Policy_____

Note: If you have more than one life insurance policy, provide the same information on all of
the policies and attach it to this sheet.

WHEN DEATH OCCURS, WHAT TO DO

B. NOTIFY MEDICAL (HEALTH) INSURANCE AGENCIES AND COMPANIES

    (1) **Medicare** (if applicable), Notification/Claims

        Phone_____ID Number_____

    (2) **Medicaid** (if applicable), Notification/Claims

        Phone_____ID Number_____

    (3) **Medical (Health) Insurance** Company(s), Notification/Claims

        Company Name_____Notification/Claims Phone_____

        Address_____

        Insured Name_____ ID Number_____

        Primary Insured (if applicable)_____ID Number_____

    (4) **Long Term Care Insurance** (if applicable), Notification/Claims

        Company Name_____Notification/Claims Phone_____

        Address_____

        Insured Name_____ ID Number_____

        Primary Insured (if applicable)_____ID Number_____

C. OTHER INSURANCE POLICIES (former military, employer, accidental, etc.)

_____

_____

D. LOCATION OF ALL INSURANCE POLICIES_____

16. REPORT DEATH OF DECEASED TO SOCIAL SECURITY ADMINISTRATION (SSA) OFFICE:

SSA PHONE <u>1-800-772-1213</u>   SSA WEBSITE <u>www.socialsecuritydeathbenefits.gov</u>

DATE OF DECEASED'S BIRTH_____DATE OF DECEASED'S DEATH_____

DECEASED'S SOCIAL SECURITY NUMBER_____

17. NOTIFY FAMILY CPA:

NAME OF CPA_____PHONE_____

CELL PHONE_____E-MAIL_____

ADDRESS_____

ADVANCE DIRECTIVES

Another big "ought to do" is to protect yourself and family from potential suffering and excessive expenses by executing advance directives, discussed in *You Only Die Once* in Chapter 3. The dramatic need for completing the appropriate forms, similar to the ones described on the following pages, is evident in hospice research. It was recently revealed that a shocking 76 percent of adult Americans have **not** put in writing how they want to be cared for at the end of life.

For example, if toward the end of your life you are unable to pay your bills, make business decisions, or care for your children and pets—who would you like to take over for you? If you are unable to communicate your wishes about your health care, who do you want to make those decisions? If you would not like to be attached to machines to keep you alive after doctors verify that you will not recover, who do you want to make that most important decision? You may unwittingly cause confusion and conflict within your family if you do not sign written directives that state how these and other life and death events will be handled in your final hours.

Do your loved ones a big favor by signing appropriate directives now. If you do, they all will know *what* you want and *who* has authority to act for you at the end of your life.

The information on pages 26-30 of *My Personal Planner,* and on pages 16-18 of *You Only Die Once,* gives you a general outline of some of the important advance directives used in the United States. They may vary from state to state, so be sure to locate the ones appropriate to your area.

Legal copies of these forms may be obtained from an attorney, mortuary, hospital, or the **American Medical Association.** You may also call the **Funeral Consumer Alliance** (FCA) at 1-800-765-0107. The FCA website is *www.funerals.org.* Another resource is the **National Hospice & Palliative Care Organization** at 1-800-658-8898. Their website is *www.caringinfo.org.*

Put your completed advance directives in the "Advance Directives" folder of your end-of-life file. And be sure to put a copy in your "Instant Action" folder!

8 IMPORTANT REASONS
TO SIGN
ADVANCE DIRECTIVES

1. Advance directives are loving favors to do for those you care about.

2. Advance directives open discussions with family members about your values and views on quality of life during the dying experience.

3. Advance directives allow you to control your own health care decisions when or if you become unable to communicate.

4. Advance directives allow your signed instructions to speak for you at the time of your death, rather than outdated laws or hospital policies.

5. Advance directives increase the likelihood that you will receive the care you want.

6. Advance directives enable you to require medical professionals to withhold or withdraw life support that would artificially prolong your life.

7. Advance directives take the pressure off family members who may be too emotional to make life or death decisions in the event of your passing.

8. Advance directives reduce the trauma, confusion, and conflict about choices that often accompany a death.

ADVANCE DIRECTIVES PRIMER

Advance directives are signed, written instructions from you about how you wish to be cared for at the end of your life.

Although there are many advance directives in use in the United States, below are general descriptions of several of the most common ones. Since states differ in their requirements for these documents, think of the descriptions here as general information—a *primer*—to get you started in thinking about these important directives. **The selections below are not the actual advance directive forms. Talk with your attorney (or another trusted advisor) to determine what directives meet your needs.**

Completing the information on these pages will help you identify and define some of the most widely used advance directives. It will also encourage you to identify reliable persons to whom you wish to give power to make decisions for you when you are unable to make them for yourself. You may grant your appointees the authority to make all decisions in certain areas of your life. Or you may limit them to specific, defined responsibilities.

It is imperative that you discuss these important issues with the people whom you plan to give this authority—to make sure they understand your wishes, accept the responsibility, and are willing to follow your instructions.

STATUTORY DURABLE POWER OF ATTORNEY

WHAT IT DOES: It delegates a competent person, whom you appoint as your agent, to act for you on **financial, business,** and/or **personal** matters if you become unable to make decisions because of disability or incapacity. This power ends at your death, at which time your will and executor take over. This document does not authorize anyone to make medical or health care decisions for you.

SAMPLE WORDING: I appoint_____
(WHOLE NAME)

Alternate_____
(WHOLE NAME)

to act for me, making decisions on **financial, business,** and/or **personal** matters, if I become unable to make these decisions for myself because of disability or incapacity.

ADVANCE DIRECTIVES PRIMER

MEDICAL POWER OF ATTORNEY FOR HEALTH CARE

WHAT IT DOES: It permits a trusted person, whom you appoint as your agent, to act for you regarding your **health care** decisions if you are unable to make such choices. This document gives your agent authority to make *specific* medical decisions or to make *any and all* medical decisions, in accordance with your specified wishes.

SAMPLE WORDING: I appoint_____
(WHOLE NAME)

Alternate_____
(WHOLE NAME)

as my agent who has authority to make any and all **health care** decisions, in accordance with my wishes, when I am no longer capable of making them myself.

DIRECTIVE TO PHYSICIANS AND FAMILY OR SURROGATES (LIVING WILL)

WHAT IT DOES: A *living will* is a signed and witnessed document that you complete when you are competent and capable of making end-of-life decisions. It goes into effect *only* if your condition is **terminal** or **permanently unconscious**. A living will allows you to direct that life-sustaining treatments be withheld or withdrawn. It directs your physicians **not to use life-sustaining procedures to keep you alive if your condition is terminal or irreversible** and the procedures merely delay your death and prolong undesirable effects. Many people are concerned that advances in medical technology may be used to extend life beyond the time when quality of life is possible.

The living will becomes effective when: (1) you are unable to make decisions; (2) your attending physician has declared your condition to be terminal; and (3) your attending physician is aware of the existence of your signed and dated living will. Usually, all three of these conditions must occur for your living will to take effect.

SAMPLE WORDING: If I have a disease or physical condition certified to be **terminal** by a physician and application of **life-sustaining procedures would only artificially prolong the moment of my death**, I direct that such procedures be **withheld** or **withdrawn** and that I be permitted to die naturally.

ADVANCE DIRECTIVES PRIMER

APPOINTMENT OF AGENT TO CONTROL DISPOSITION OF REMAINS

WHAT IT DOES: It permits you to appoint an agent to make any or all decisions about the **disposition of your remains** after your death, in accordance with your specified wishes.

SAMPLE WORDING: I appoint_____
(WHOLE NAME)

Alternate_____
(WHOLE NAME)

as my agent who will have authority upon my death to make decisions about the **disposition of my remains.**

APPOINTMENT OF GUARDIAN FOR MINORS AND/OR DISABLED ADULTS

WHAT IT DOES: This directive allows you to appoint someone to care for and make decisions and provisions for **minors or disabled adults** for whom you are responsible at the time of your death or incapacity.

SAMPLE WORDING: I appoint_____
(WHOLE NAME)

Alternate_____
(WHOLE NAME)

as guardian to make decisions after my death concerning **minors or disabled adults** for whom I have been responsible.

OUT-OF-HOSPITAL (OOH) DO NOT RESUSCITATE (DNR) ORDER

WHAT IT DOES: This directive is for use outside a hospital or medical facility. It is for the purpose of **instructing emergency medical personnel and other health care professionals to abstain from resuscitation attempts.** This will permit you to have a natural death with peace and dignity, if you are in a state of decline where there is no chance of recovery, and death is imminent.

WILL PREPARATION

An up-to-date will is the cornerstone of your estate. Yet, 70 percent of American adults do not have one. A thoughtful will is one of the priority items listed on the "Location-Location-Location" page (*My Personal Planner*, page 11), and of course is included in your master end-of-life plan. Many would argue that it is number one. It is the final expression of a person's values.

If you die without a will, the court will name an executor of your estate. In turn, the executor may hire lawyers, accountants, tax advisors, and any other needed experts—all at your heirs' expense. What is left in your estate will be distributed according to state law. Very likely, it will not end up the way you would have wished.

An out-of-date will can cause serious problems for your survivors. Especially when important changes have occurred in your life, such as a birth, death, or divorce.

I am not an attorney, so I will not be giving you legal advice. But I hope to motivate you to do all the necessary planning and engage the legal advisors you need for leaving your heirs the gift of a comprehensive and effective will.

Since estate laws are complicated and are different in each state, it is best to get legal counsel in the state where you live. Before interviewing an attorney, get several recommendations for him/her from people you respect.

Choosing your executor is also a very important decision. Give this selection careful thought and prayer; your decision could have long-lasting consequences. Since this person will administrate your will after you die, it is essential that you discuss it with him/her while questions can be answered and issues clarified.

Your will is a very legalistic document, so I strongly suggest that you write separate and caring messages of love and appreciation to those important to you. But do not make these personal missives a legal part of your will. Prepare an extra folder to preserve these love messages, so they can be delivered after your death.

PREPARING MY WILL

Guidelines

These pages provide guidelines to assist me in getting my will drawn up. They don't replace my need for qualified legal help to prepare it. If possible, I will engage an attorney for this purpose. If that is not possible, I will purchase a package of *will* information at an office supply store, or search on-line for "Last Will and Testament" forms and assistance.

It is especially important that I read Chapter 5 of *You Only Die Once* **before** and **as** I work through these guidelines. Pages 33-36 will prepare me to begin. Pages 36-45 will help me, step by step, through this very important process.

As I work my way through the guidelines, I will mark the places that call for a check (√). My check mark verifies that I have made the appropriate decision or taken the appropriate action required. Also, I will fill out the blanks asking for information. While I am doing this, I will be laying the groundwork for myself and my attorney to prepare my will. This process can be useful whether I am working on my original will or updating my old one.

PROVERB: "A MAN WHO DIES WITHOUT A WILL HAS LAWYERS FOR HEIRS."

---

1. SELECTING MY ATTORNEY (*You Only Die Once*, pages 37-38)

   A. Check one of the following:

   I need a general law/family law attorney. ____
   (√)

   I need a certified estate-planning specialist. ____
   (√)

   B. Several people I trust have recommended the following attorney to prepare my will:

   His/Her name is_____Phone_____

   C. I have set an interview with the following attorney: Mr./Ms._____

   Date_____Time_____Location_____

   He/She has agreed to do this initial interview without charge. ____
   (√)

   (Repeat B and C until I settle on my attorney of choice.)

   D. The attorney I have selected to prepare my will is: Mr./Ms._____

   Phone_____FAX_____E-Mail_____

   Mailing Address_____ ____
   (√)

PREPARING MY WILL

2. INFORMING MY ATTORNEY (*You Only Die Once*, pages 38-40)

My attorney will need the following information:

A. A list of my assets (real estate, investments, etc.) and debts (credit cards, mortgages, etc.)

Date given to my attorney_____ _____
(√)

B. The division and designation of my assets to my heirs

Date given to my attorney_____ _____
(√)

C. The name of my executor (and alternate executor) with appropriate information regarding him/her (Section 3 below)

Date given to my attorney_____ _____
(√)

D. A written or typed description of what appeals to me as the best ways to go about leaving my estate in an orderly and loving fashion, noting special approaches to be taken with specific heirs (in view of changes, like divorce or death, that may call for careful and sensitive attention in stating the terms of my will, especially in light of any previous understandings and legal documents)

Date given to my attorney_____ _____ _____
(√)

3. CHOOSING MY EXECUTOR (*You Only Die Once*, pages 40 and 41)

My executor is the person I will name **before** I die to carry out the instructions in my will **after** I die. Read, study, and *contemplate* the executor information on pages 36, 40, and 41 in *You Only Die Once*. My executor is more than "very important" to me. He or she will "stand in" for me after I am gone. When I have made my selection and received agreement from my person of choice, I will provide the following information to my attorney and to the special others who should know:

My Executor's Name_____Phone_____

Address_____

Cell_____E-Mail_____

Alternate Executor's Name_____Phone_____

Date given to my attorney_____ _____
(√)

PREPARING MY WILL

4. REVIEWING/REVISING ATTORNEY'S DRAFT OF MY WILL (*You Only Die Once*, page 41)

Review and revise my attorney's draft of my will until: *(a)* **I understand it** and *(b)* **I am satisfied that it says what I want it to say.**

Date I gave revised draft to my attorney_____ _____
(√)

5. REVIEWING, REVISING, AND **SIGNING** MY WILL (*You Only Die Once*, page 42)

Date I signed my will_____ _____
(√)

6. PUTTING MY WILL IN A SAFE PLACE (*You Only Die Once*, page 42)

There is no rule requiring that I retain copies of my will at all the locations mentioned below. I should, however, select enough storage and preservation places that it may easily be found and accessed. Make a check (√) by each location I select below:

A. My attorney,_____, is retaining an original signed copy
(NAME)
of my will at his/her office. Address_____

Phone_____ Completion Date_____ _____
(√)

B. An original signed copy of my will is in my end-of-life plan file, located at_____

_____.

Completion Date_____ _____
(√)

C. An original signed copy of my will is in a safe-deposit box at_____.

The following persons have bank-approved access to this safe-deposit box_____

_____.

Completion Date_____ _____
(√)

D. Other locations of a signed copy of my will are _____

_____

_____.

Completion Date_____ _____
(√)

PREPARING MY WILL

7. CHANGING MY WILL (*You Only Die Once*, page 43)

I should review my will on a regular basis. When major changes occur (i.e. births, deaths, marriages, divorces, inheritances, financial value, or insurance policies), I will make necessary amendments to coincide with my present situation. Many changes can be made inexpensively through legal attachments, made by my attorney and signed by me.

8. ESTABLISHING AN INTERIM FUND (*You Only Die Once*, page 43)

I should create an *interim fund* to cover both the normal and unexpected costs that occur at the time of my death. Of course, there are funeral and burial/cremation expenses. But there may be other costs, such as hospital, nursing home, surprise medical expenses, or bringing family members to the services. If I am able, I should save my loved ones painful anxiety and costs by setting aside a fund devoted only to giving financial relief in these situations. I may do this with a cash reserve or perhaps with a small life insurance policy. Check one of the options below:

A. I have established an interim fund at_____ _____

    in the amount of $_____. Complete information for accessing this fund is in a file

    folder marked **Interim Fund**, located in my end-of-life file.

              Completion Date_____ _____
                                                        (√)

B. For an interim fund, to cover immediate expenses at the time of my death, I have purchased

    a life insurance policy from_____in the amount of $_____.

    Copies of this policy are located both in my "Insurance" folder and "Interim Fund" folder

    in my end-of-life plan file, as well as in my safe deposit box at_____

              Completion Date_____ _____
                                                        (√)

C. Describe here an alternate choice I have made for providing an interim fund. _____

_____

             Completion Date_____ _____
                                                       (√)

FINANCIAL STATEMENTS

What Financial Statements Can Do for You

Do financial duties scare you? Money matters are intimidating to most people. Some folks fear that filling out a personal financial statement will reveal failures in their judgment, or poor choices. I hear people say, "I don't want to know how bad things are, so I never reconcile my bank statements or record my financial situation."

But here is some good news. When you have the right information in hand, putting together and maintaining your personal financial records is not so difficult. Once you have filled out a financial statement, keeping it updated annually becomes a much easier task. Basically, it consists of knowing what you *own*, what you *owe*, what *income* you can reasonably expect, and your *expenses*. The following five pages provide forms to help you become familiar with your financial picture:

1. ASSETS—what you own. What you have in the bank, savings accounts, employee pension plans, insurance policies, value of home, vehicles, etc.

2. DEBTS—what you owe. Home mortgages, auto loans, business and personal loans, credit card debt, etc.

3. INCOME ESTIMATE—sources and amounts of income (including spouse), so you will know what money will be coming in.

4. EXPENSES—payments of your regular living expenses, like groceries—and your debt obligations, like your mortgage payment. This way, you will know what money will be going out.

Preparing financial statements is one of the surest ways to avoid financial pain. If you have a personal accountant or CPA, be sure to consult her/him as you complete this process.

In filling out the following forms, try to be as accurate as possible. Use the information that is mailed to you concerning loans, mortgages, credit cards, etc. If you don't know an exact amount, make your best estimate. When you have completed your financial statements, knowing where you stand financially will give you great satisfaction.

Financial Statement Form
ASSETS

On this form you will make a list of your assets—the property, money, investments, life insurance policies, and other "things of value" that you own. Everyone's holdings are different, so you may need to use this form as a model while adapting it to your own profile. For instance, if you have four insurance policies, they will hardly fit on line 12. So adapt or restructure this to meet your needs.

In the the VALUE column, enter the most accurate dollar amount available to you as the *cash* or *market value* of each item. If you must estimate, be conservative.

	LOCATION*	PHONE/E-MAIL**	ACCOUNT NO.**	VALUE
1. HOME:				$
2. BUSINESS:				$
3. OTHER REAL ESTATE:				$
4. CHECKING ACCOUNTS:				$
5. CASH:				$
6. SAVINGS ACCOUNTS:				$
7. CD'S:				$
8. IRA/ROTH IRA:				$
9. STOCKS/BONDS:				$
10. EMPLOYEE PLAN(S):				$
11. VEHICLES/BOATS, ETC:				$
12. INSURANCE POLICIES:				$
				$
13. OTHER ASSETS: (antiques, jewelry, art, tools, etc.)				$
				$
				$
				$

*ADDRESS OR COMPANY
**IF APPLICABLE

Date:_____

Total Assets $_____

NOTE: Update this form annually, or when major changes occur (i.e., the death of your spouse).

Financial Statement Form
DEBTS

	LENDER	PHONE/E-MAIL	ACCOUNT NO.	DEBT AMOUNT
1. HOME MORTGAGE:	_____	_____	_____	$_____
2. OTHER MORTGAGES:	_____	_____	_____	$_____
	_____	_____	_____	$_____
3. AUTO LOANS:	_____	_____	_____	$_____
	_____	_____	_____	$_____
4. BUSINESS:	_____	_____	_____	$_____
5. PERSONAL LOANS: (with or without contracts)	_____	_____	_____	$_____
	_____	_____	_____	$_____
	_____	_____	_____	$_____
6. CREDIT CARDS:	_____	_____	_____	$_____
	_____	_____	_____	$_____
	_____	_____	_____	$_____
7. OTHER:	_____	_____	_____	$_____
_____	_____	_____	_____	$_____
_____	_____	_____	_____	$_____
_____	_____	_____	_____	$_____
_____	_____	_____	_____	$_____

*Calculating Your Net Worth: If your total assets are greater than your total debts, you have a positive net worth. Enter the positive difference on the Net Worth line. If your total debts are greater than your total assets, you have a negative net worth. Enter the negative difference on the Net Worth line—enclosed by parentheses ( ). The parentheses indicate negative net worth.

Total Debts: $_____

Total Assets: $_____
(FROM PREVIOUS PAGE)

Date:_____

Net Worth:* $_____

Financial Statement Form
INCOME ESTIMATE

This form will help you estimate two important income totals—the first from your **present income** sources, and the second from your probable **future income** potential, as follows.

Left Column: Your **Present Annual Income**. Whether you are married, single, retired, not retired, semi-retired, or otherwise. In most cases, spouses should show joint income.

Right Column: Your **Future Annual Income**. A life-altering event (like retirement, death, disability, etc.) can affect your (or your spouse's) expected future income. It is impossible to foresee all these potential outcomes (or their combinations); so just fill in this column as best you can, with your likely future changes in mind. Your numbers won't be entirely correct, but they will give you helpful preparation for your time ahead.

Each spouse, or other person, should complete his/her own form. The assistance of a CPA or attorney can be very helpful, especially for residents of community property states. Whether income from each source is received monthly, quarterly, or otherwise, compute each to an annual sum for this report. Explain income sources/special circumstances in the space provided after each item.

PRESENT ANNUAL INCOME		FUTURE ANNUAL INCOME
$_____	1. SALARY/WAGES:_____	$_____
$_____	2. PENSIONS:_____	$_____
$_____	3. SOCIAL SECURITY:_____	$_____
$_____	4. INTEREST:_____	$_____
$_____	5. DIVIDENDS:_____	$_____
$_____	6. ANNUITIES:_____	$_____
$_____	7. OTHER BUSINESS INCOME:_____	$_____
$_____	8. OTHER SOURCES OF INCOME:_____	$_____
$_____	**GRAND TOTAL**	$_____

Financial Statement Form
LIVING EXPENSE BUDGET (Standard)

Knowing and recording your expenses (monthly and periodic), can help you budget your resources. Below is a general listing of commonly experienced expenses. If the form on this page adequately serves your purposes, use it. If it does not, then use the form on the next page to develop your own customized "Living Expense Budget" report.*

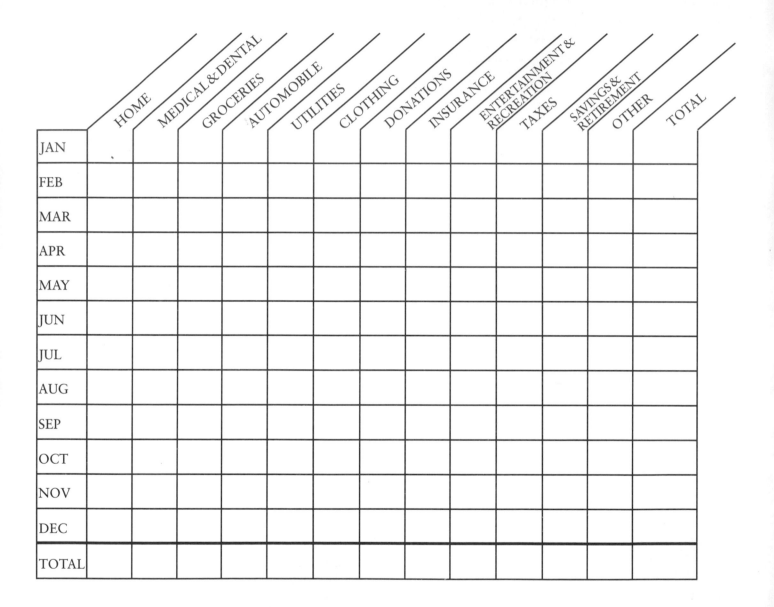

	HOME	MEDICAL & DENTAL	GROCERIES	AUTOMOBILE	UTILITIES	CLOTHING	DONATIONS	INSURANCE	ENTERTAINMENT & RECREATION	TAXES	SAVINGS & RETIREMENT	OTHER	TOTAL
JAN													
FEB													
MAR													
APR													
MAY													
JUN													
JUL													
AUG													
SEP													
OCT													
NOV													
DEC													
TOTAL													

*Important Note: Some expense items consist of several parts. For instance, "Home", for you, may include items like mortgage payment, maintenance, and homeowner's fee. So that you don't have dozens of columns on your expense report, attach a page to the back of your report that lists any sub items that go into any regular category on your report. This will significantly simplify your expense reporting process.

Financial Statement Form
LIVING EXPENSE BUDGET (Custom)

Use this form to customize your "Living Expense Budget". Simply fill in your own expense categories.

	TOTAL													TOTAL
JAN														
FEB														
MAR														
APR														
MAY														
JUN														
JUL														
AUG														
SEP														
OCT														
NOV														
DEC														
TOTAL														

9 REASONS

FINANCIAL STATEMENTS ARE IMPORTANT

1. They tell you what you own.

2. They tell you what you owe.

3. They tell you what income you can expect.

4. They tell you your expenses.

5. They give you more control over your life.

6. They help you make wiser decisions about spending and saving.

7. They help you plan better for big future needs—cars, house, vacations, and retirement.

8. At the time of your death, financial statements provide a wonderful gift to your loved ones, reducing emotional conflict and helping them know what they have.

9. They allow you to relax and live more bodaciously now, knowing your financial plan is in place.

ANTICIPATING MY FINAL DAYS

A friend told me, "I want to live to be 100...and healthy". Maybe that's what most people hope. Even if you achieve that goal, you *will* come to the end of your life at some time. Your final stage of life can last a few moments or several years. Preparing for that phase and anticipating your final days can be a blessing for you and your family.

Years ago, families lived closer together and aging parents often lived with their adult children. When I was growing up in Kentucky, my grandparents lived next door to us until Grandma died. Then Grandpa moved into our home. For me, it felt special and complete to have him at our family table. Grandparents living with their children and grandchildren add a wonderful dimension for everyone. However, it is not always possible to live with family members; so it is important to be familiar with other options.

To help you find peace and meaning at the end of your life, look at the check list below to aid in making good choices for your sunset days. You might not know the answers right now, but it is helpful to be thinking about available options. Also, you might want to talk with family members, a counselor, or your minister about these issues.

Placing checks (√) in the blanks below may ease you into anticipating your final days.

1. Have I spoken with my family about my thoughts, feelings, and wishes for my final days?
   Yes____ (√) No____ (√)   Do I want to talk with someone about this topic?   Yes____ (√) No____ (√)

2. I would like to live my final days: In my home, with caregivers to help me? Yes____ (√) No____ (√)
   With a family member?   Yes____ (√) No____ (√)   In a caring facility?   Yes ____ (√) No____ (√)   Do I
   want to talk with someone about this topic?   Yes____ (√) No ____ (√)   Who? _____

3. So family members will know my wishes, should I write them a letter of permission about how I want to be cared for, if I become incapacitated? Yes____ (√) No____ (√)   Do I plan to write a letter like this? Yes____ (√) No____ (√) If "yes", when will I write this letter? _____

4. Have I examined possible caregiver options, such as home-care services, assisted living facilities, continuing care retirement communities, or other possibilities? Yes____ (√) No____ (√)   Do I want to get more information on all possibilities? Yes____ (√) No____ (√)

5. Have I set aside financial resources to pay for my end-of-life care? Yes____ (√) No____ (√)   Do I want to talk with someone about doing this? Yes____ (√) No____ (√) Who? _____

At age 95, my dad went into a nursing home. It was not because he had to be there, he said, but because he was planning ahead for his final days. For free copies of *Guide to Senior Housing and Care* in your area, contact New Lifestyles at 1-800-869-9549 or visit www.NewLifeStyles.com.

THE ART OF CAREGIVING

Just as it is important to anticipate your own final days, it is wise to prepare for the possibility that you may become the caregiver for someone else. It may be for only a few days or weeks—or it could be months or years of a loved one's life. Following is a brief primer to minimally prepare you for such an experience.

A. ASSESS THE SITUATION:
   1. **Ask** the patient questions about his/her needs.
   2. **Observe** the patient to determine what tasks he/she can do without assistance.
   3. **Learn,** from A1 and A2, how to deal with the patient's activities of daily living—like dressing, eating, personal hygiene, memory problems, driving, paying bills, and ambulation.

B. BUILD A SUPPORT TEAM:
   1. **Select** a small group of unselfishly concerned people—like family, friends, neighbors, church people, and health professionals—for information and sharing of duties.
   2. **Name** one person as "Care Manager" to oversee the total plan.

C. ORGANIZE A LOOSE LEAF NOTEBOOK:
   1. **VIP Information Records,** including contact information about doctors, hospitals, support group members, family, minister(s), and other emergency sources of assistance
   2. **Patient's Medication List,** with instructions for giving meds and keeping records
   3. **Procedures/Restrictions,** with clear records of instructions about things to do and/or not to do in caring for the patient
   4. **Journal of Activities and Tasks,** to be planned and recorded upon completion (This will become a clearing house for all activities for the patient and each member of the support team, so everyone will be on the same page.)

D. UTILIZE COMMUNITY RESOURCES:
   Such as Meals On Wheels, adult day care, and public transportation assistance

E. REGULAR REVIEW WITH PATIENT:
   To evaluate how the plan is working, and to keep family members informed

THE ART OF CAREGIVING

F. TAKE CARE OF YOURSELF:

Caregivers frequently devote themselves totally to those they care for and, in the process, neglect their own needs. Pay attention to yourself—so you will be a healthy caregiver.

G. LONG-DISTANCE CAREGIVING:

If you are a long-distance caregiver, you are among approximately seven million adults who care for aging parents who do not live close by, according to the National Institute on Aging (a good resource, 1-800-222-2225, www.nia.nih.gov). Only decades ago, most people lived out their lives in or near the communities of their birth. Now, adult children of the elderly are more likely to live many miles from them, so that "long-distance" caregiving becomes necessary. Below are a few guidelines for effective long-distance caregiving.

1. Make a personal visit to your parents' (or others') residence, and assess the situation.

2. Communicate with family about the patient's needs—asking for input and assistance.

3. Contact your parents' primary care physician for a medical assessment.*

4. Obtain local phone books for resource references.

5. Explore volunteer and professional agencies and services in the local area.

6. Create an information journal, with important phone numbers, medications, doctors, etc.

7. Keep caregivers and physicians advised about changes in your parents' situation.

8. Anticipate the need to relocate them. Look at all options (i.e. assisted living), including costs.

9. Plan visits, phone calls. Send emails, photos, large print books, CD's, etc.

10. Download a copy of AARP's booklet, *Prepare to Care, A Planning Guide for Families*, at www.aarp/foundation/preparetocare. For more details, call AARP at 1-800-687-2277.

*VERY IMPORTANT: Review pages 26-30 of *My Personal Planner*, and Chapter 3 of *You Only Die Once*, for information about advance directives that patients must have in order for you/others to assist them. Federal laws to protect patient privacy require specific written advance directives in these matters.

OBITUARY INFORMATION

Everybody Needs An Obituary

An obituary serves as acknowledgement to friends, associates, and all others who knew the deceased—that a significant person has lived and died. And it announces the time and place of the celebration service(s) to be held. Rather than just listing names of survivors and dates, I wish obituaries could be enhanced to tell more about the deceased person's life. Of course, I am aware that the cost of publishing obituaries is increasing each year. You pay by the number of lines you use; so it can be a dilemma.

After filling out the information on page 47, think about how to use it in writing your obituary in story form. Who else can better reflect on your life, accomplishments, and highlights? Amusing stories and humor add a special flavor. Preparing this notice in advance is a gift to your family. When a death occurs there are so many tasks that need to be done (in a short time under emotional stress) that the obituary can become a difficult chore. My husband and I wrote each other's obituaries. When he read what I had written, he said: "Wow! I can hardly wait to die and have people hear this!"

In the book, *You Only Die Once*, Chapter 7, I call this information "Writing Your Ultimate Bio." You may want to review this chapter while working on the obituary form on the next page. The completed form provides the basic information that a newspaper needs. It is also helpful when applying for death certificates.

You can recognize when a person's obituary is written by someone who did not know the deceased, by the vague reporting on the person's life and death. So give it a try, and write what *you* would like to have in the newspaper about you after you die.

MY OBITUARY FORM

MY FULL NAME:_____

ADDRESS:_____

DATE OF BIRTH:_____ PLACE OF BIRTH:_____

FATHER'S NAME:_____ MOTHER'S MAIDEN NAME:_____

MY EDUCATION:_____

EMPLOYMENT:_____

FRATERNAL ORGANIZATIONS:_____

HONORS/SPECIAL RECOGNITIONS:_____

PUBLIC SERVICE:_____

SPECIAL ACHIEVEMENTS:_____

MILITARY SERVICE:_____

MARITAL STATUS: SINGLE_____ MARRIED_____ WIDOWED_____
                        (√)   (√)   (√)

NAME OF SPOUSE (indicate if deceased): _____

WEDDING DATE:_____ PLACE:_____

NAMES AND ADDRESSES (cities and states) OF CHILDREN:_____

_____

NAMES OF GRANDCHILDREN:_____

_____

NAMES OF SIBLINGS:_____

_____

MEMORIALS/CHARITIES FOR GIFTS:_____

PHOTO WITH OBITUARY: YES_____ NO_____
                            (√)   (√)

PLACE(S) AND TIME(S) OF: VIEWING_____

SERVICE_____

BURIAL_____SCATTERING ASHES _____

PUBLISH OBITUARY IN: NEWSPAPERS, ALUMNI MAGS., TRADE JOURNALS, COMPANY NEWSLETTERS, ETC.

_____

_____

(Remember, information from your eulogy on the next two pages can also be used in your obituary.)

EULOGY

A Tribute To Your Life

A eulogy is a tribute of praise, a testimonial, usually given at the funeral/memorial service by a family member or friend of the deceased.

Who could write the most colorful and flamboyant story of your life? I believe you could!

If you are like a lot of people I know, the very thought of writing a "tribute of praise" to yourself is distasteful. It might sound like blowing your own horn, which my dad always said was a "no-no". But before you say no thanks to this great idea of mine, at least try looking at it through a different lens.

The term *tribute of praise* is the usual definition of a eulogy. In most cases, someone has to throw it together on short notice. So typically, along with selective truths about the departed, things are included like exaggerated attributes, imagined accomplishments, and, occasionally, downright created events that did not even happen. Carried too far, this kind of thing makes people snicker silently during the service.

Now, you don't want that, even if everything said about you is absolutely wonderful.

What if you write your own eulogy—and talk mainly about the good things in your life? The things you're really glad you did, even proud of. Especially the ones you truly enjoyed, that made you smile and laugh and cry for joy. Making quilts for your grand babies; playing in an all-star game; your first kiss; earning scout awards; making pull-taffy as a kid; your first promotion on the job; singing in the choir; and, for sure, talking about a few of the most important people in your life.

No, don't tell all the bad stuff. This is a eulogy, not a confession. Tell the soul-stirring truth about the good stuff, and people attending your memorial service will smile and feel they know you even better. Of course, it won't hurt to tell a few things "on yourself" that were unusually embarrassing or funny... or to acknowledge your imperfections.

When you're writing, include highlights, accomplishments, limited family history, your passions, and your philosophy of life. Be sure to add humor that made you laugh and interesting incidents you experienced along your pathway. Also, be open about painful experiences in your life, without being maudlin.

This tribute will be a treasured memory for those who love you. And the information you gather for the eulogy will be helpful in writing your obituary.

You can honor a close family member or special friend by asking her/him to read what you've written in your service. If you're bodacious, make a CD or DVD of yourself personally delivering your own eulogy. Remember—your memorial service is a *celebration* of your life.

PREPARING MY EULOGY
A Celebration Of My Life

Write a colorful story of my life. Include important people, highlights, accomplishments, interests, and my philosophy of life. Begin by gathering information in the seven categories below. Then use these resources to develop an informative and fascinating mini-autobiography. Keep it brief enough for a funeral or memorial service. This is a eulogy; so be nice to myself.

1. BRIEF STORY OF MY PARENTS:_____
_____
_____

2. MEMORIES OF MY CHILDHOOD:_____
_____
_____

3. MY TEEN YEARS AND EARLY ADULTHOOD:_____
_____
_____

4. MARRIAGE AND FAMILY:_____
_____
_____

5. MY CAREER:_____
_____
_____

6. EMPTY NEST STAGE AND OLDER YEARS:_____
_____
_____

7. ACCOMPLISHMENTS MOST SATISFYING TO ME: _____
_____
_____

Planning Your
GRANDE FINALE

Funeral/Memorial Service—Burial/Scattering Observance—Reception

After a loved one's death, survivors—with crumpled hearts and clouded minds—are burdened with numerous hurried and emotional decisions. Then, there remain optional plans for a funeral (or memorial) service, a burial (or scattering) observance, and a reception. What a relief it will be for them if you have already made these plans when their time comes to grieve and honor your passing!

Funeral Home and Cemetery Costs: Among the first things you might do in this planning is select funeral home and burial professionals to provide the assistance your loved ones will need. This will mean doing comparative cost studies of funeral homes and cemeteries in the area where your last earthly celebration is likely to take place. It will be particularly helpful if you *shop before you drop*—get to know your options and the related costs so you can make wise choices. I suggest you invite a friend to go with you. Visit funeral homes and cemeteries to get an idea of their services. What is involved and what the costs will be. Collect price lists of their services and record them on the forms on pages 51-52, so you can make realistic price comparisons. After all, we shop and compare for other major life events. Why not this one? Burying a lot of money in the ground may not be what you want.

Planning Your Funeral/Memorial Service and Burial/Scattering Observance: By the time you complete your cost planning, likely you will have decided whether you prefer a traditional funeral service or, instead, a memorial service. A funeral service usually is held within a few days after death and before burial. It is also customary—though not required—for the casket (open or closed) to be present. A memorial service is usually held at a later date, without the presence of a casket. Your decisions about this service may be influenced by your preferences about burial and/or cremation and the possible scattering of ashes. The forms on pages 53-57 are designed to help you make your own decisions, plan your services, and relieve your loved ones of a great deal of stress.

The Reception After Your Funeral: Think of the reception after your funeral (or other) service as your going-away party—as your last hurrah. What kind of gathering would please you? It can be as simple as coffee and cookies or a catered meal with all the trimmings. It can be held in a church, funeral home, restaurant, or family home. It can include only family and close friends or be open to all who attend the services. Make sure your loved ones know that you have made these plans, where they are kept, and the provisions you have made to pay for them. *My Personal Planner,* pages 58-59, will help with ideas.

Most people who attend funeral/memorial services don't realize the amount of time and energy involved in the planning and decision-making for these events. You will be leaving a special gift to survivors if you make your plans ahead of time. Chapters 8, 9, and 10 in *You Only Die Once* offer valuable guidance in making your choices. I believe you will discover this to be a satisfying journey, and a relief...knowing your final arrangements will be a **grande finale!**

FUNERAL COST SURVEY
To Help Me Make
MY CHOICE OF FUNERAL HOMES

	FUNERAL HOME A	FUNERAL HOME B
FUNERAL HOME NAME:	_____	_____
PHONE NUMBER	_____	_____
SERVICE OPTIONS:		
ADMINISTRATION FEES	$_____	$_____
TRANSPORT BODY TO FUNERAL HOME	$_____	$_____
TRANSPORT BODY TO OTHER FACILITY	$_____	$_____
TRANSPORT FAMILY TO CEMETERY	$_____	$_____
TRANSPORT FLOWERS TO CHURCH	$_____	$_____
TRANSPORT FLOWERS TO CEMETERY	$_____	$_____
POLICE ESCORT	$_____	$_____
CASKET	$_____	$_____
VAULT OR GRAVE LINER	$_____	$_____
BODY PREPARATION:		
REFRIGERATION/EMBALMING	$_____	$_____
BATHING	$_____	$_____
HAIR	$_____	$_____
COSMETOLOGY	$_____	$_____
CLOTHING	$_____	$_____
OTHER FUNERAL EXPENSES:		
VISITATION PER DAY	$_____	$_____
CHAPEL (if used for funeral services)	$_____	$_____
MEMORIAL BOOK/CARDS	$_____	$_____
NO. OF DEATH CERTIFICATES NEEDED ____	$_____	$_____
FUNERAL/MEMORIAL SERVICE FEE	$_____	$_____
GRAVESITE SERVICE FEE	$_____	$_____
_____	$_____	$_____
_____	$_____	$_____
TOTAL FUNERAL COSTS:	$_____	$_____

MY CHOICE OF FUNERAL HOME: _____
FUNERAL HOME NAME   ADDRESSS   PHONE NUMBER

THREE IMPORTANT NOTES: 1. IT MAY BE BETTER TO GET MORE THAN TWO SURVEYS. MAKE COPIES OF THIS FORM AS NEEDED. 2. REVISE THIS INFORMATION AT LEAST EVERY FIVE YEARS. 3. KEEP ALL INFORMATION GATHERED IN THIS SURVEY AND ATTACH IT TO THIS FORM—BEFORE YOU PLACE IT IN YOUR END-OF-LIFE FILE. THEN, WHEN YOU REVISE THE INFORMATION, IT WILL BE MUCH EASIER.

CEMETERY COST SURVEY
To Help Me Choose
MY BURIAL SERVICES AND CEMETERY

	CEMETERY A	CEMETERY B
CEMETERY NAME:	_____	_____
PHONE NUMBER	_____	_____
BURIAL EXPENSES:		
BURIAL PLOT	$_____	$_____
OPENING/CLOSING GRAVE	$_____	$_____
MAUSOLEUM	$_____	$_____
MARKER/INSTALLATION	$_____	$_____
INSCRIPTION	$_____	$_____
CREMATION COST:		
CREMATION	$_____	$_____
URN	$_____	$_____
SCATTER ASHES	$_____	$_____
EARTH BURIAL	$_____	$_____
MAUSOLEUM	$_____	$_____
COLUMBARIUM	$_____	$_____
MARKER/INSTALLATION	$_____	$_____
INSCRIPTION	$_____	$_____
OTHER EXPENSES:	$_____	$_____
_____		
_____	$_____	$_____
_____	$_____	$_____
CEMETERY COSTS TOTAL:	$_____	$_____

MY CHOICE OF CEMETERY:_____

CEMETERY NAME   ADDRESSS   PHONE NUMBER

THREE IMPORTANT NOTES: 1. IT MAY BE BETTER TO GET MORE THAN TWO SURVEYS. MAKE COPIES OF THIS FORM AS NEEDED. 2. REVISE THIS INFORMATION AT LEAST EVERY FIVE YEARS. 3. KEEP ALL INFORMATION GATHERED IN THIS SURVEY AND ATTACH IT TO THIS FORM—BEFORE YOU PLACE IT IN YOUR END-OF-LIFE FILE. THEN, WHEN YOU REVISE THE INFORMATION, IT WILL BE MUCH EASIER.

FUNERAL/MEMORIAL SERVICE
PROGRAM OPTIONS

Before you plan your funeral or memorial service, it will be helpful to look over a list of program elements that often are used in services for grieving survivors and friends. Your purpose will be to begin identifying personal preferences for the kinds of things you would like in your own service.

First, read through the **OPTIONS** list below. Check (√) **Yes, Maybe,** or **No** after each item.

Next, in the **OTHER OPTIONS** spaces, list elements you would like in your service that are not on the **OPTIONS** list. *Think freely and creatively.* If need be, add a second page.

═══ OPTIONS ═══

	YES	MAYBE	NO		YES	MAYBE	NO
1. MUSIC:				**5. AUDIO AND/OR VIDEO PRESENTATIONS:**			
PREAMBLE	___	___	___				
VOCALIST/GROUP	___	___	___	PICTURES	___	___	___
CHOIR	___	___	___	SLIDES	___	___	___
CONGREGATIONAL	___	___	___	AUDIO	___	___	___
POST-SERVICE	___	___	___	VIDEO	___	___	___
2. PRAYER:				**6. EULOGY:**	___	___	___
OPENING	___	___	___	**7. SERMON:**	___	___	___
PASTORAL	___	___	___	**8. CLOSING REMARKS:**	___	___	___
BENEDICTION	___	___	___	**9. INVITATIONS:**			
3. READING:				RECEPTION	___	___	___
SCRIPTURE	___	___	___	OTHER	___	___	___
OTHER	___	___	___	**10. PROCESSIONAL TO CEMETERY:**	___	___	___
4. TESTIMONIALS:				**11. GRAVESIDE SERVICE:**	___	___	___
FAMILY	___	___	___				
FRIENDS	___	___	___				

═══ OTHER OPTIONS ═══

YES	MAYBE	NO		YES	MAYBE	NO
___	___	___		___	___	___
___	___	___		___	___	___
___	___	___		___	___	___
___	___	___		___	___	___
___	___	___		___	___	___

Now you are ready to turn the page and plan your very own services!

MY FUNERAL/MEMORIAL SERVICE PREFERENCES

1. MY PLAN FOR: FUNERAL SERVICE____ MEMORIAL SERVICE____
     _(√) _(√)
   OPEN CASKET____ CLOSED CASKET____ NO CASKET____
     _(√) _(√) _(√)

2. PRINTED PROGRAM (for order of service, songs, obituary, scriptures, etc.): YES____ NO____
     _(√) _(√)

3. PERSON TO OFFICIATE: NAME_____
   RELATIONSHIP/POSITION/TITLE_____ PHONE_____

4. LOCATION OF SERVICE (church, funeral home, or other):_____
   CONTACT PERSON_____ PHONE_____
   ADDRESS_____ E-MAIL_____

5. SPECIAL INSTRUCTIONS: MY BURIAL CLOTHING_____
   JEWELRY_____
   GLASSES ON____ OFF____ OTHER_____
     _(√) _(√)

6. EULOGIST: NAME_____ PHONE_____
   READ THE EULOGY I WROTE ____ PLAY THE CD OR DVD I PROVIDED ____
     _(√) _(√)
   WRITE AND PRESENT THE EULOGY ____ OTHER_____
     _(√)

7. LIST SELECTED READINGS, SCRIPTURES, PRAYERS, POEMS, ETC. I WISH TO BE PRESENTED:
   _____
   _____

8. PARTICIPATION BY OTHER SELECTED INDIVIDUALS (names/phones/roles in order):_____
   _____
   _____

9. PALLBEARERS (names/phones):_____
   _____
   _____

10. REPRESENTATIVES OF: EMPLOYER, CIVIC GROUPS, FRATERNAL ORGANIZATIONS, ETC.
    (names/organizations/titles/roles in my funeral or memorial service)_____
    _____
    _____

MY FUNERAL/MEMORIAL SERVICE PREFERENCES

11. INSTRUMENTAL MUSICIANS (organist, pianist— names, phones):_____
_____

12. VOCALISTS (soloist, group—names, phones):_____
_____

13. FAVORITE MUSIC SELECTIONS TO BE PERFORMED IN SERVICE:_____
_____
_____

14. OTHER MUSICIANS (names, roles, phones):_____
_____

15. TAPED BACKGROUND MUSIC: YES____ NO____ FAVORITE SONGS/ARTISTS_____
                                  (√)   (√)
_____
_____

16. CONGREGATIONAL SINGING: YES____ NO____ PRINT LYRICS IN PROGRAM: YES____ NO____
                                (√)   (√)   (√)   (√)
_____
_____

17. ATTENDEES TO SIGN SIGNATURE BOOK: YES____ NO____
                                          (√)   (√)

18. WHAT TO INCLUDE IN PROGRAM (all elements of the service in order, including ideas not mentioned on this form): _____
_____
_____
_____
_____
_____
_____

DO YOUR PLANS ADEQUATELY COVER EVERY PART OF YOUR SERVICE? YES____ NO____
                                                                  (√)   (√)

MY BURIAL/CREMATION SERVICE PREFERENCES

1. MY PLAN FOR: BURIAL SERVICE____ CREMATION SERVICE____
   (√)   (√)

   OPEN CASKET_____ CLOSED CASKET_____ NO CASKET_____
        (√)   (√)   (√)

   If you checked CREMATION SERVICE *above, skip to item #10.*

2. CEMETERY: NAME _____

   ADDRESS_____PHONE_____

3. CEMETERY/FUNERAL HOME CONTACTS (names and phones):_____

   _____

4. PERSON TO OFFICIATE: NAME _____

   POSITION/TITLE_____PHONE_____

5. PALLBEARERS: SAME AS FUNERAL/MEMORIAL SERVICES? YES_____ NO_____
                                                                              (√)   (√)

   (IF YOU CHECKED "NO", GIVE NAMES AND PHONES)_____

   _____

   _____

   _____

6. BURIAL/GRAVESIDE SERVICE INCLUDES (i.e., music, comments, prayer):_____

   _____

   _____

7. SPECIAL RITUALS AT GRAVE SITE (examples: readings, singing, gun salute, release of balloons
   or butterflies, scattering rose petals):_____

   _____

8. SERVICE DECORATIONS (like flowers, hobby articles, photos, other): _____

   _____

9. OTHER INSTRUCTIONS:_____

   _____

   _____

MY BURIAL/CREMATION SERVICE PREFERENCES

10. FOR CREMATION—CEMETERY/FUNERAL HOME CONTACTS (names and phones):_____

_____

_____

11. BURIAL OF REMAINS IN CEMETERY: YES____ NO____
    (√)   (√)

    CEMETERY NAME_____

    CONTACT PERSON_____PHONE_____

    _____

12. SCATTERING OF REMAINS: YES____ NO____ LOCATION _____
    (√)   (√)

    _____

    CONTACT PERSON_____PHONE_____

13. COAST GUARD PHONE NUMBER OR OTHER CHOICE FOR SCATTERING OVER WATER:

    _____

14. RITUALS AT SCATTERING:_____

    _____

    _____

15. MAUSOLEUM BURIAL: NAME OF MAUSOLEUM_____

    CONTACT PERSON_____BURIAL TIME_____

    LOCATION _____

16. OTHER INSTRUCTIONS:_____

    _____

    _____

    _____

RECEPTION AFTER THE FUNERAL

Your Going-Away-Party

A reception is usually held after a funeral or memorial service. But you can have yours any time it fits your needs and wishes, and those of your loved ones. It will provide an opportunity for people to gather, remember, talk, and feel connected to the others who cared about you. It will allow them to replay joyful and loving memories.

Sometimes the reception is a private event for family members and selected friends only. Other times, it is open to everyone who attends the memorial/funeral/burial/scattering service. The speaker offers an invitation to join the family for the reception after the service. It can be held in a church parlor, funeral home, private home, garden, museum, or restaurant—anywhere that offers a comfortable atmosphere to reflect on the life and personality of the loved one and friend.

Why not plan your own going-away-party? It can be a simple affair of coffee and donuts, or a catered event. Some people plan a party in a home or public place where there is dancing and celebration. If you do this, make sure the occasion reflects *your* wishes.

Remember reading about the going-away-party for Charles Schulz, creator of the "Peanuts" comic strip? The crowd was offered chocolate chip cookies and root beer—standard fare for Snoopy and the Peanuts gang after their ball games.

At some receptions, special videos and slide presentations about the deceased may be shown, making for a warm intimate experience. You can be creative! Plan a reception that will be remembered long after you are gone.

Some folks prefer a simple reception or open house. Usually, tributes are made and toasts offered. Those attending are encouraged to share stories and memories of their loved one.

There are many options. Write down your ideas on the form on the next page, and choose the person you would like to be in charge of this special affair. You might even plan the event together. If an elaborate reception is planned, several people may be involved. You might list a number of friends you think would enjoy helping create the reception that will honor you. The form on the next page will aid in your planning. Think of it as your "going-away-party".

RECEPTION AFTER THE FUNERAL

My Going-Away-Party

MY NAME: _____

1. PERSON IN CHARGE OF MY RECEPTION: NAME_____

   PHONE_____ E-MAIL_____

2. RECEPTION LOCATION: _____

3. WHO IS INVITED? FAMILY_____ FRIENDS_____ EVERYONE AT THE SERVICE_____
   (√)   (√)   (√)

4. RECEIVING LINE: YES____ NO____ WHO IS IN IT?_____
   (√)   (√)

   _____

5. FOOD/REFRESHMENTS:_____

   _____

6. MUSIC:_____

   _____

7. VIDEO/SLIDES/PICTURES:_____

   _____

8. DECORATIONS:_____

   _____

9. SPECIAL READINGS, POEMS, SCRIPTURES, STORIES:_____

   _____

   _____

10. OTHER INSTRUCTIONS:_____

    _____

    _____

THE GRIEVING PROCESS

Mourning is the process of adapting to the inevitable losses that occur in life. Sooner or later you are going to have to face the issue of your own death. But you may also have to cope with the death of a loved one—and most people are unprepared for their reactions to such a loss. Often months of depression will follow. You feel empty, lost, and out of control. Returning to normal seems impossible. I have heard grieving people ask: "Am I there yet?" Hardly ever do ordinary coping skills adequately prepare someone for this kind of life-altering situation.

You may become more aware of your own mortality and vulnerability. Fear and emotional involvement with the finality of any severe loss can be the catalyst for some strange behavior.

Chapter 15, "Hope for Survivors", in *You Only Die Once,* discusses the stages of grief. Understanding these stages can help survivors move through the grieving process.

Six stages of grief are listed on the next page. These reactions to a major loss are as normal as tears, and become part of the healing process. Knowing you will go through many grief feelings is part of recovery before fully regaining a sense of reality—and finally reaching a new normalcy.

The sequence may be different for different people. The grief stages are not always distinct from one another, and they can merge together. But everyone goes through a coping struggle. A wide range of feelings and sensations will accompany passage toward reclaiming hope for the future. The start of healing is evident when you can get back into the routine of life, doing what needs to be done, and taking care of practical and emotional matters that need attention. That's what I call reaching a *new normalcy.* Just as before, it is not perfection. It is being able, again, to juggle your various responsibilities and pleasures without losing your balance.

Survivors often fail to realize that the grieving process is normal and healthy. It provides a road to recovery. So when you experience grief, watch for the following (or similar) stages.

STAGES OF GRIEF

1. KICK IN THE BELLY:
    SHOCK
    DISBELIEF

2. RUNNING FOR COVER:
    SEARCHING FOR ESCAPE

3. KICKING BACK:
    LOOKING FOR A SCAPEGOAT

4. IF ONLY:
    THINKING SOMETHING I DID CAUSED THE DEATH
    THINKING SOMETHING I DID NOT DO CAUSED THE DEATH
    ("If onlys" can't be changed. They avoid reality.)

5. BOOMERANGS AND HEALING:
    THE SURPRISES OF REMEMBERING
    THE HEALING OF RELIVING MEMORIES

6. REACHING FOR A NEW NORMALCY:
    STANDING AGAIN
    REGAINING BALANCE
    ACCEPTING LIFE CHANGES
    MOVING ON

Note: Not all of these stages will apply to everyone.

COMMUNICATION IN TIMES OF CRISIS

Mastering the Art of Condolence

At the time of a significant loss, condolences are some of the most difficult words to say or write. Some people freeze and can't speak to the grieving. They don't know what to say or what to do, so they do nothing. This feels like rejection to mourners.

Others resort to clichés which can sound harsh, hurtful, or insincere. When someone has lost a child or a significant other person, it does not feel loving to hear, "It's God's will." Or to be told, "It's for the best." Or, "You are so lucky you have other children." Or, "Call me if you need anything." Although the people who say these things mean well, it does not feel good to the grieving person.

Our world needs to rethink how to communicate with mourners. People who are grieving usually yearn to feel a loving touch, to hear the words, "I'm so sorry." One of the greatest gifts at the time of a loss may be the presence of someone who will just let a person grieve and listen to the stories of what occurred.

Other caring gestures might include baby sitting, taking the dog for a walk, cleaning up the kitchen, making a list of people who have sent food.

The cue cards on the following page provide words to say and things to do that might feel more loving to a person going through a loss.

Chapter 13, in *You Only Die Once*, discusses the dilemma of not knowing what to do or what to say at the time of a crisis, and provides helpful suggestions.

CUE CARDS

Suggestions for What to Say and What to Do
To Comfort Grieving People

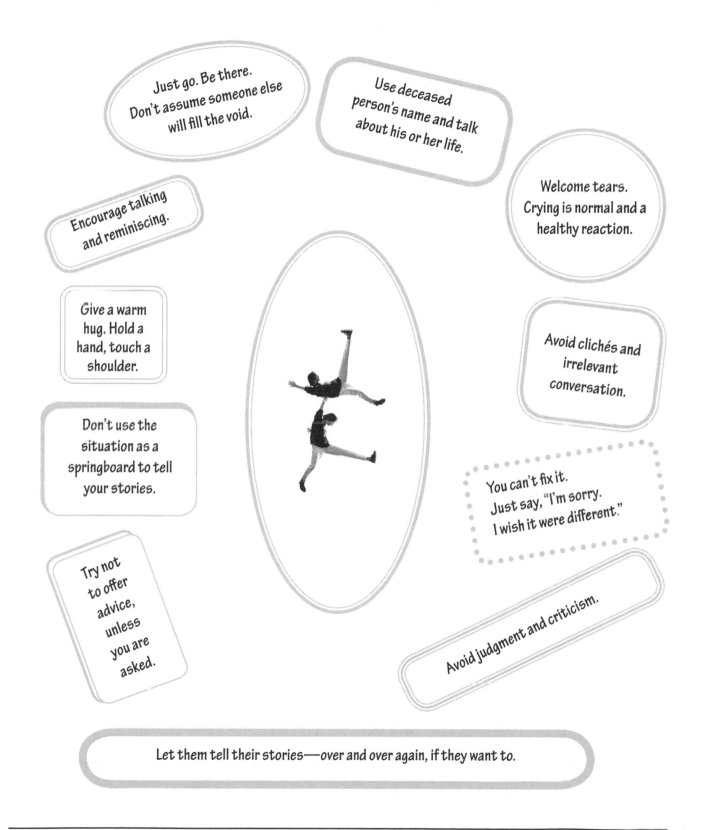

Just go. Be there. Don't assume someone else will fill the void.

Use deceased person's name and talk about his or her life.

Encourage talking and reminiscing.

Welcome tears. Crying is normal and a healthy reaction.

Give a warm hug. Hold a hand, touch a shoulder.

Avoid clichés and irrelevant conversation.

Don't use the situation as a springboard to tell your stories.

You can't fix it. Just say, "I'm sorry. I wish it were different."

Try not to offer advice, unless you are asked.

Avoid judgment and criticism.

Let them tell their stories—over and over again, if they want to.

CHERISHED POSSESSIONS

A Practical Way To Help Your Loved Ones

Treasured items, when passed on to others, create opportunities within families to connect the past with the future—like passing the torch from one generation to another. Valued possessions can carry on a sense of history, love, and faith long after the people they represent are gone.

Most everyone has items of special interest: a lovingly marked Bible, a handmade chest or quilt, a ruby ring, an antique pocket watch, or family photographs. Sometimes, the story or the history of a possession is more precious than the monetary value. You may be the only one who knows why an item is important to you. The meaning of a unique possession may be lost forever if you don't write down the reasons it is prized, and how you happen to own it.

The manner in which you pass on your possessions can add to the pleasure for both parties. One idea is to make an event out of it—like a private tea at which you present a piece of family jewelry to a loved one. Treat it as an opportunity to give significance to your valued items by enhancing your relationship with a much-loved family member or friend. Special holidays or events can be occasions for giving cherished possessions.

Presenting your precious items to loved ones before you die is a bonus for everyone. Not only does it distribute your belongings, but when you give while you live—you know where they go.

"Your Cherished Possessions," Chapter 6 in *You Only Die Once*, provides interesting background for this subject. It suggests creative ideas for presenting treasured items to your loved ones.

On the next page, "Distribution of My Cherished Possessions," list the items you want to give to someone. Write the stories behind them, and why they are important to you. Then think about who you would like to have each one when you no longer need it.

DISTRIBUTION OF MY CHERISHED POSSESSIONS

MY CHERISHED POSSESSIONS AND THEIR STORIES OR HISTORIES	GIVE THEM TO
Example: Gold pocket watch in middle drawer of roll top desk, given to me by my grandfather, Isaac Fish, on my 21st birthday, May, 1905.	NAME: *Grandson, Bob Jenkins, on his* EVENT/DATE: *21st birthday, Sept. 1976*
	NAME: EVENT/DATE:
	NAME: EVENT/DATE:
	NAME: EVENT/DATE:
	NAME: EVENT/DATE:
	NAME: EVENT/DATE:
	NAME: EVENT/DATE:
	NAME: EVENT/DATE:

My Name _____ Signature _____ Date _____

(Note: WHITE-OUT THE EXAMPLE, AND COPY THIS PAGE FOR MORE ITEMS.)

DEVELOPING YOUR SUPPORT CIRCLE

Who Can You Turn To?

Being connected to others is an important ingredient to living a satisfying and meaningful life. A support system is an inventory of people you can turn to for encouragement, motivation, advice, and entertainment—a cadre of "atta-boy" cheerleaders.

The goal of a good support circle is to identify relationships you have in different categories of your life—and not depend on one or two persons to provide all your needs. That's unrealistic.

By filling in "My Support Circle" on the next page, you are identifying your network of important people. They are the ones who enable you to celebrate life, and to grow, prosper, live, and love. In each category fill in the names of those from whom you receive support. This support circle reminds you of the people involved in your life. It can also help you recognize areas where you may want to add more support.

You are in charge of developing your own support system. Make sure you build one that will energize and stimulate you to feel plugged into meaningful relationships.

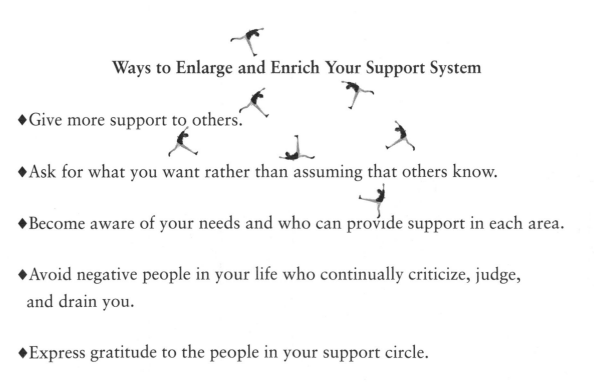

Ways to Enlarge and Enrich Your Support System

♦ Give more support to others.

♦ Ask for what you want rather than assuming that others know.

♦ Become aware of your needs and who can provide support in each area.

♦ Avoid negative people in your life who continually criticize, judge, and drain you.

♦ Express gratitude to the people in your support circle.

MY SUPPORT CIRCLE

Relationships: Cornerstones Of Happiness

INSTRUCTIONS: Put my name in the center circle. In each category, list important people in my life, past and present.

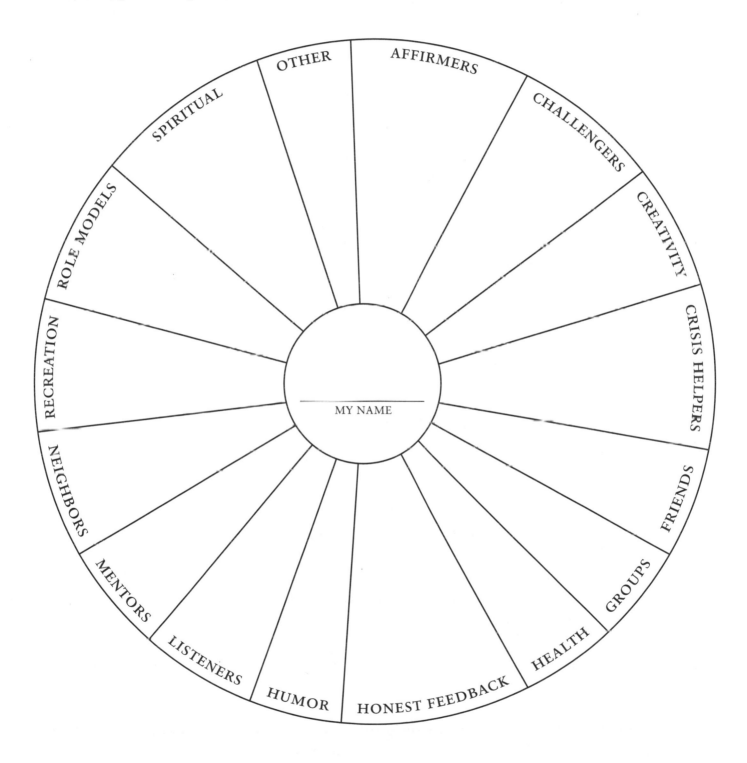

CREATING YOUR LIFELINE OF CELEBRATIONS

Examining Your Past, Present, and Future

One significant way to celebrate your life is to remember and appreciate your past. Events that happened in the years before have enriched your life. They have given you freedom, choices, experiences, and a broader understanding of the world.

On the following pages, by visiting "Where I've Been," "What I've Learned," and "Planning My Future," you can better celebrate the past and build a bold and colorful future. Past memories bring increased joy and satisfaction. Remembering accomplishments, highlights, and important decisions creates an album of a life well-lived. What you learned from parents, friends, holiday celebrations, and significant changes has shaped your life. Learning gained from life experiences and relationships *molds future generations*.

Many people enjoy writing about their past, including childhood memories, games played as a kid, important relationships, special events, favorite foods, or unique clothes they remember. Recall travels that took you around the world or around the town.

Beliefs, attitudes, and expectations are passed on from one generation to another. Many of us are unaware of the history of our value system—why we behave the way we do. Changes in the world during a lifetime have great influence on the way we think and live. Does your memory go back before TV, computers, or heart transplants? How have these events affected your life?

And what about plans for your future? Looking forward is important. Living bodaciously multiplies joy, and it's good for your health. Add spice and color to your normal routine by looking at available options and choosing the best ones for you.

Bodacious ideas make your life juicier. Jump on the "Planning My Future" forms on pages 74-76 and get moving. Action leads to a positive mood and valuable self-actualization. *Never stop dreaming*. Dreaming is the wellspring of planning. It is the spark to imagination and accomplishment, enabling you to exceed your expectations. To increase satisfaction in life, it is important to create enjoyable events to anticipate. If you plan an interesting future, it is far more likely to happen...than if you don't.

Where you've been, what you've learned, where you're going: these are the makings of your lifeline.

Chapter 16 in *You Only Die Once* will help stimulate you to live life bodaciously with grace and gusto. Remember! You're still here, so you're not finished yet.

MY LIFELINE OF CELEBRATIONS

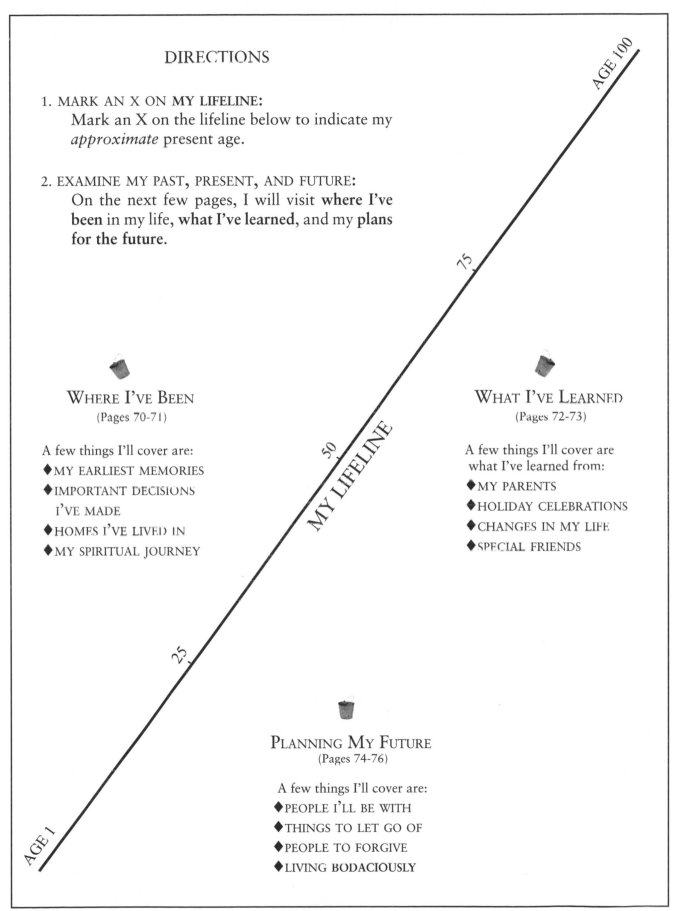

DIRECTIONS

1. MARK AN X ON **MY LIFELINE:**
   Mark an X on the lifeline below to indicate my *approximate* present age.

2. EXAMINE MY PAST, PRESENT, AND FUTURE:
   On the next few pages, I will visit **where I've been** in my life, **what I've learned**, and my **plans for the future.**

WHERE I'VE BEEN
(Pages 70-71)

A few things I'll cover are:
◆ MY EARLIEST MEMORIES
◆ IMPORTANT DECISIONS I'VE MADE
◆ HOMES I'VE LIVED IN
◆ MY SPIRITUAL JOURNEY

WHAT I'VE LEARNED
(Pages 72-73)

A few things I'll cover are what I've learned from:
◆ MY PARENTS
◆ HOLIDAY CELEBRATIONS
◆ CHANGES IN MY LIFE
◆ SPECIAL FRIENDS

PLANNING MY FUTURE
(Pages 74-76)

A few things I'll cover are:
◆ PEOPLE I'LL BE WITH
◆ THINGS TO LET GO OF
◆ PEOPLE TO FORGIVE
◆ LIVING BODACIOUSLY

AGE 1 · 25 · 50 · MY LIFELINE · 75 · AGE 100

WHERE I'VE BEEN

Recollections

On this page and the next, write about important memories from my life.

1. MY EARLIEST MEMORIES, LIKE, MY VERY FIRST MEMORY; GAMES I PLAYED AS A KID; MY FIRST DAY AT SCHOOL; A PAINFUL EXPERIENCE; AND A TIME WHEN I KNEW SOMEONE LOVED ME:_____

_____

_____

_____

_____

_____

_____

2. IMPORTANT DECISIONS THAT CHANGED MY LIFE, LIKE, ACCOMPLISHMENTS; AT LEAST ONE FAILURE IN MY LIFE; DIFFICULTIES I OVERCAME; AND TURNING POINTS:_____

_____

_____

_____

_____

_____

3. MEMORIES OF SPECIAL PEOPLE IN MY LIFE, LIKE, PARENTS; GRANDPARENTS; CLOSE FRIENDS; ADVERSARIES; TEACHERS/PROFESSORS; MINISTERS; BUSINESS ASSOCIATES; SPOUSE(S); AND OTHERS:____

_____

_____

_____

_____

_____

WHERE I'VE BEEN

Recollections

4. MY TRAVELS, LIKE, PLACES I WENT (what made them fascinating and enjoyable); VISITING A FAMILY MEMBER OR AN OLD ACQUAINTANCE; VACATIONS; AND BUSINESS TRIPS:_____

_____

_____

_____

_____

_____

5. MEMORIES OF THE HOMES I'VE LIVED IN (including neighbors):_____

_____

_____

_____

_____

_____

6. MY SPIRITUAL JOURNEY AND PHILOSOPHY OF LIFE:_____

_____

_____

_____

_____

_____

7. OTHER IMPORTANT MEMORIES AND EVENTS IN MY LIFE:_____

_____

_____

_____

WHAT I'VE LEARNED

Lessons of My Life

1. IMAGINE MY GRANDCHILDREN, OR OTHERS CLOSE TO ME, LISTENING TO ANECDOTES ABOUT MY LIFE. WRITE DOWN AT LEAST ONE STORY I WOULD LIKE TO PASS ON TO THEM:

_____

_____

_____

_____

_____

_____

2. ATTITUDES AND BELIEFS I'VE LEARNED FROM MY PARENTS:_____

_____

_____

_____

_____

_____

3. WHAT I'VE LEARNED FROM RELIGIOUS HOLIDAYS AND OBSERVANCES

   (Christmas, Hanukkah, Ramadon, etc.):_____

_____

_____

_____

_____

_____

WHAT I'VE LEARNED

Lessons of My Life

4. WHAT I'VE LEARNED FROM MY FRIENDS AND RELATIONSHIPS:_____
    _____
    _____
    _____
    _____
    _____
    _____
    _____
    _____
    _____

5. CHANGES I WOULD MAKE IF I COULD LIVE MY LIFE OVER:_____
    _____
    _____
    _____
    _____
    _____
    _____
    _____
    _____

6. MAJOR WORLD CHANGES WHICH HAVE AFFECTED MY LIFE:_____
    _____
    _____
    _____
    _____
    _____

PLANNING MY FUTURE

Springboards to Bodacious Living

1. ACTIVITIES I ENJOY:_____
   _____
   _____

2. PEOPLE WITH WHOM I WANT TO SPEND MORE TIME:_____
   _____
   _____

3. SOME THINGS I CAN DO TO IMPROVE RELATIONSHIPS:_____
   _____
   _____

4. VOLUNTEER ACTIVITIES I WILL EXPLORE:_____
   _____
   _____

5. SOME THINGS I WANT TO LET GO OF:_____
   _____
   _____

6. SOME THINGS I WANT TO DO MORE:_____
   _____
   _____

7. ACHIEVEMENTS I AM GOING TO CELEBRATE:_____
   _____
   _____

PLANNING MY FUTURE

Springboards to Bodacious Living

8. WAYS I CAN MAKE MYSELF MORE INTERESTING, LESS IRRITATING, AND MORE LOVABLE:

   MORE INTERESTING_____

   _____

   LESS IRRITATING_____

   _____

   MORE LOVABLE_____

   _____

9. WAYS I CAN IMPROVE MY SPIRITUALITY:_____

   _____

   _____

   _____

10. BLESSINGS I PLAN TO ENJOY:_____

   _____

   _____

11. SOME PEOPLE WHO HAVE WRONGED ME THAT I WANT TO FORGIVE:_____

   _____

   _____

12. PEOPLE FROM WHOM I NEED TO ASK FORGIVENESS:_____

   _____

   _____

13. WAYS I WILL TRY TO BE MORE PASSIONATELY CURIOUS:_____

   _____

   _____

PLANNING MY FUTURE

Springboards to Bodacious Living

14. ACTIVITIES THAT WILL KEEP ME LEARNING AND GROWING:_____

_____

_____

15. WAYS I WILL SHOW MORE APPRECIATION:_____

_____

_____

16. IDEAS I CAN USE TO PUT MORE HUMOR AND FUN IN MY LIFE:_____

_____

_____

17. CHANGES THAT WILL MAKE MY LIFE MORE BODACIOUS:_____

_____

_____

_____

_____

18. ONE THING I WILL DO THIS WEEK TO LIVE MORE BODACIOUSLY:_____

_____

_____

_____

_____

_____

_____

Now that you've completed *My Personal Planner*, here's a note to you from the author, Margie Jenkins...

Congratulations! You have prepared for the end of your life, with *grace* and *gusto*. Thank you for using *My Personal Planner* and for taking time to record your choices before it's too late.

What a wonderful gift you have created for your loved ones...and for yourself. And I hope you found it thought-provoking and satisfying to review your options for living out your final days.

So, my dear friend, relax—knowing that you have done your best to reduce the traumatic burden of decision-making for you and your family when you reach your final chapter. I encourage you to use the next three pages to influence your loved ones and friends to follow your example. They too can enrich their lives by using *My Personal Planner* to make their own end-of-life decisions.

If this journey has been rewarding for you, perhaps you would like to help as many as you can to enjoy the same experience. The next three pages are designed to assist you in doing just that.

Dear Reader,

I am deeply gratified by responses from people like you who have read *You Only Die Once,* and have worked through *My Personal Planner.*

Often I hear something like: "I thought it could only be painful to go through the experience of preparing for my death, but, with *My Personal Planner*, it has been such a wonderful, releasing experience. In some ways, it's actually been fun."

Then others tell me of loved ones and friends they hope to inspire to enjoy the same experience. Hearing these comments so often, I was stirred to write the next page. It is a list of things someone is likely to learn from *You Only Die Once* and *My Personal Planner*. It's not for you—you already know the whole list. It's more for that special person you would like to have the same rewarding sense of achievement you are enjoying right now.

On the back of the list there's a note "from you" to your friend/loved one. If you would like to use it, just fill in his/her name on the blank spaces in the note. Then sign yours at the bottom in the same personal way you usually finish your notes or letters to them. You may either copy the page or snip it out and mail it. Or if you want to give them a gift copy of one or both of the books, put the note/list in with your gift. (You may want to write your own letter. That would be best of all.)

Thank you so much for helping me to help others find lots of unexpected joy in planning their end-of-life years. And just think of how many of their friends and loved ones will be grateful to you too!

We can all learn that planning for life's ending is just as important as planning for life's beginning.

With much love and sincere thanks!

Margie
Margie Jenkins

A Special Note to someone I love and care about…

Dear _____,

Promise not to laugh or think I've turned strange and eerie. I've been doing something I've long known should be on my "to-do" list"—but it was just too foreboding to even think about. So I put it off, again and again.

Then I heard about Margie Jenkins' books, *You Only Die Once* and *My Personal Planner*. Really, they are about—don't cringe—*planning for your own death*.

Okay _____, now laugh if you wish. Because that's just what I found myself doing as I read these books and thought about preparing for the last pages of my life.

Yes, there were also times when I felt sad or scared or nervous. But overall, it was a surprisingly enjoyable and rewarding experience. I cannot exaggerate how good I feel about what these books have done for me. They have totally changed the way I anticipate my own death and, especially, the way I will live the rest of my life.

I urge you to read *You Only Die Once*. Then decide whether you would like to use *My Personal Planner*. At the very least, read the list on the back of this note.

Much love,

YOU CAN LEARN HOW TO

1. IMPROVE YOUR UNDERSTANDING OF THE **SIGNIFICANCE OF YOUR LIFE**

2. **REDUCE CONFUSION AND EMOTIONAL TRAUMA** FOR YOUR LOVED ONES AT THE TIME OF YOUR DEATH

3. CREATE YOUR OWN **END-OF-LIFE PLAN**

4. UNDERSTAND THE IMPORTANCE OF **ADVANCE DIRECTIVES**

5. UNDERSTAND YOUR NEED FOR **A THOUGHTFUL WILL**

6. ENJOY THE PLEASURE OF DECIDING WHO WILL RECEIVE YOUR **CHERISHED POSSESSIONS,** AND THEIR STORIES

7. ANTICIPATE HOW YOU WILL SPEND YOUR LIFE WHEN YOU ARE **UNABLE TO LIVE ALONE**

8. PLAN YOUR OWN **FUNERAL/BURIAL SERVICES**

9. KNOW **WHAT TO SAY AND WHAT TO DO** WHEN TALKING WITH SOMEONE WHO IS SERIOUSLY ILL OR DYING

10. KNOW **WHAT TO DO** AT THE TIME OF YOUR LOVED ONE'S DEATH

11. IDENTIFY AND ORGANIZE YOUR **VITAL PAPERS** (will, advance directives. insurance policies, etc.)

12. **DISCUSS YOUR END-OF-LIFE PLANS** WITH YOUR FAMILY AND THE EXECUTOR OF YOUR WILL

13. CREATE **LASTING MEMORIES** THAT WILL LIVE ON IN WAYS YOU NEVER EXPECTED

14. RECOGNIZE **STAGES OF GRIEF,** AND THEIR BENEFITS, WHEN RECOVERING FROM THE DEATH OF A LOVED ONE

15. APPRECIATE THE **IMPORTANCE OF SPIRITUALITY**

When you fully understand the importance of these issues, you will be better prepared to experience life's ending with grace and gusto. You and your loved ones will be empowered to *flourish*, rather than merely survive life's most difficult circumstances.

Read the book

and use

YOU ONLY DIE ONCE...

MY PERSONAL PLANNER